Easy Quick Snacks

Low Carb Creations
for Kids
of all ages

More than 50 Nutritious Snack Recipes

by
Jackie Bible
and
Lori Overmyer

Dreams and **Motivation** *Publishing, Inc.*
Wabash, Indiana

Visit the authors' web site at _www.easylowcarbcreations.com_.

Bible, Jackie
   Easy low carb creations: more than 50 nutritious snack recipes / by Jackie Bible and Lori Overmyer. Wabash, Indiana: Dreams and Motivation Publishing, Inc., c2004.
96p.
Includes index and appendices.
ISBN 0-974926-7-9
1. Children – Nutrition. 2. Cookery – Juvenile literature. 3. Low carbohydrate diet – recipes. I. Overmyer, Lori. II. Title.
TX652   2004
641.5123   2004110930

Easy
Low Carb Creations
   for kids

Note: Every effort has been made to provide an accurate nutritional analysis of every ingredient and recipe in this book. However, since nutritional content varies for different brands of ingredients, and other variables impact nutritive value of foods, nutritive contents in this book are approximate. The authors and publisher are in no way liable for food allergies or other medical problems incurred as a result of using recipes in this book. Before starting an exercise program or special diet, one should always consult a physician.

Specific brand names mentioned as utilized in testing of recipes are recommended and are copyrighted by those companies.

Dedication

Easy Low Carb Creations For Kids *is dedicated to those kids who struggle with being overweight. We both know many kids who are teased, left out of "the group" and have their feelings hurt because of their size. Our hope is to provide a tool to help kids of all ages (adults included) who are struggling with weight loss.*

We also dedicate our low carb snack recipes to "our kids" who struggle with the desire for sweet foods and are diabetic. **Easy Low Carb Creations For Kids** *gives you yummy options.*

To all, we are pleased to provide recipes that encourage good health and taste great. Snack food does not equal junk food. We hope this book helps people enjoy eating snacks that are not the common high sugar, high carb foods. This book is dedicated to those who value good-tasting snacks and good health.

Easy
Low Carb Creations
for kids

Letter to Parents or Guardians

Dear Parent or Guardian,

    Is your child a junk food junkie? Does he/she skip a nutritious *breakfast*, not taking time to *break* last night's *fast*? Are potato chips, candy, cookies, pizza, snack cakes, breakfast pastries, and regular soda pop typical snacks? Is your child one of the millions of overweight kids, or have the family history to become an overweight adult? Does your child have diabetes or have a genetic predisposition to adult onset diabetes? If any of your answers are yes, using **Easy Low Carb Creations For Kids** can help.

    Every day, I teach young people who say yes to all of the above, and I hope to empower you to help your children; to make more answers to the above questions NO! Students complain they are hungrier if they eat breakfast. I explain that high carb foods such as sugar and refined grains are digested quickly, but eggs, meat and other high protein foods are digested more slowly and their fat content helps us feel full longer. Others skip breakfast to lose weight. I explain that eating a low carb, high protein breakfast every morning starts the process of burning food which leads to weight loss, and adding exercise will improve health as well as increase their metabolism.

    Many kid approved low carb breakfast casserole recipes can be found in **Easy Low Carb Creations**, Lori Overmyer's and my first cookbook. These can easily be baked ahead of time, refrigerated and reheated in the microwave oven on busy mornings.

    Educate your children about nutrition; just give them the basics. Healthy foods help us have healthy bodies. Dairy products help build strong bones and teeth. Protein, found in such foods as meats, fish, poultry, eggs, cheese and dairy products build strong muscles and help

Easy **Low Carb Creations** *for kids*

us grow. Fruits and vegetables are needed to keep us healthy and help other foods do their jobs. Whole grains provide important vitamins and fiber. Junk food, such as sugar and too many simple carbohydrates, is not good for our bodies.

Obesity is now the greatest single cause of death in the United States. Heart disease, high blood pressure, strokes, some forms of cancer and diabetes are all risks associated with being overweight. You protect your child from obvious danger, but often a child's diet is overlooked. Knowing they eat a nutritious lunch and dinner may seem good enough. However, current research and childhood obesity rates point out it's NOT GOOD ENOUGH.

Okay, so you're on board to providing your child with a low carb breakfast because you understand the benefits, and you have purchased **Easy Low Carb Creations For Kids** to solve the snack dilemma. Now, stop buying junk food. If only nutritious, low carb snacks are available, that's what your kids will eat.

Easy Low Carb Creations For Kids is a great cookbook for a child learning to cook or for those who like quick, easy snacks. Symbols are used to indicate the difficulty level of each recipe and if it takes more or less than 15 minutes to prepare. The kitchen can be a dangerous place to an unsupervised child using equipment without proper instructions and experience. Help your child be safe, learn to enjoy cooking and be proud of his/her food **creations**. Encourage your child to follow directions carefully and only prepare recipes within their ability level. Please read the Introduction to Kids page, and advise your child in using this book. Model safe work and sanitation habits; remember, you are your child's first nutrition and food preparation teacher. Enjoy working with your child in the kitchen; wonderful memories are **created** there.

Sincerely,
Jackie Bible

Easy Low Carb Creations
for kids

You Are The Proud Owner of **Easy Low Carb Creations**
So Let's Get *Start*ed!
For Kids...

We have written this book to help you be healthy by learning to cook yummy snacks that are good for you. You cannot become the brightest **star** by eating sugary junk foods. We hope you will be safe, have fun and learn to **shine** in the kitchen. Before you **star**t to cook, read this page and pages 8-17 carefully. As you choose a recipe, make sure it matches your cooking skill level. Read the list of ingredients carefully and make sure you have everything you need. Read the directions carefully, and ask an adult if you have any questions. You are on your way to becoming a super**star**!

The following symbols will help guide you to food preparation **star**dom...

Rising Stars *are recipes for you if you have never cooked or have done very little cooking by yourself. You will only use hand tools and the microwave oven to make these foods. No use of knives, electric mixers, electric blenders or the range is needed for these simple recipes.*

Shining Stars are recipes for you if you have some cooking experience. You will need to be able to safely use a knife, electric mixer, electric blender and microwave oven. No use of the range is needed for these recipes.

Shooting Stars are recipes for more experienced cooks. You will need to be able to safely use all of the above tools and appliances, as well as an oven, stovetop and broiler to prepare these recipes.

Easy
Low Carb Creations
for kids

Table of Contents

Benefits of Eating Healthy Foods 8-9

How to Eat Low Carb 10

Recommended Dairy/Nuts/Seeds 11

Recommended Fruits and Vegetables 12

What If Guide 13-15

Sanitation/Food Preparation Terms 16

Cooking Terms/Measuring 17

Cookie Stars 19-25

Dipping Stars 27-31

Frozen Stars 33-39

Liquid Stars 41-45

Meal Making Stars 47-61

Salty Crunchy Stars 63-73

Sweet Stars 75-83

Veggie Stars 85-90

Index 91-93

Author Information 94

What the Experts Say/Order Information 95

Watch for these symbols to help you plan!

When you're **star**ving, these recipes take less than 15 minutes to prepare.

< 15

Start now but eat later, since these recipes take more than 15 minutes to prepare.

15

Easy Low Carb Creations for kids

Starring...benefits of eating healthy foods:

Protein helps your body grow, repair damaged parts, fight disease and gives you energy. Your bones, muscles, skin, eyes and hair are made of protein.

★ **Protein Stars**: beef, pork, poultry (chicken, turkey, etc.), fish, shellfish, eggs, and dairy foods (milk, cheese, yogurt, etc.), dry beans and peas, whole grain products, nuts, peanut butter and seeds

Carbohydrates (carbs) give you energy and some carbs have fiber. Fiber helps you have bowel movements, reduces risk of colon cancer and helps keep your blood healthy.

★ **Fiber Stars**: fruits and vegetables (eat any edible skins on apples, peaches, cucumbers etc.), whole wheat and wheat bran products, dry beans, dry peas and oat products

Natural sugars give us energy and are found in fruits, dairy and whole grain foods.

Fat helps you have healthy skin, is needed for normal cell growth, helps vitamins do their jobs, gives you energy and helps you feel full longer.

★ **Fat Stars**: butter, sour cream, salad dressings, chocolate, meats, nuts, seeds, peanut butter, egg yolks, whole milk, cream, half-and-half and cheese.

Vitamins are needed for protein, fat and carbs to do their jobs. They also keep your nervous system working, help keep you from getting diseases, help make your blood, bones, skin and teeth, and help you feel good.

★ **Vitamin Stars**: vegetables such as broccoli, spinach, cabbage and carrots; fruits such as cantaloupe, peaches, oranges, and strawberries; fortified vitamin D milk; and whole grain foods.

Minerals make up your teeth and bones, are needed for your nervous system, blood, fluid balance and for your muscles to work (your heart is a very important muscle).

★ **Mineral Stars**: dairy foods, meat, fish, eggs, nuts, seeds, dark green leafy vegetables, fruits and whole grain foods.

Water is the most important nutrient; your blood is 80 percent water. Water keeps your body temperature normal and is needed for the other nutrients to do their jobs. You should drink 8 glasses of water every day.

How to eat low carb...

I make sure I eat more protein than carbs whenever I put food in my mouth. For example, when eating fruit, I eat cottage cheese, meat, an egg or cheese. I also limit the amount of healthy carbs I eat, so there is no room in my diet for worthless carbs. I don't want to be a **Falling Star**, so I don't eat refined sugars or many starches.

People Become Falling Stars by eating **refined sugars** – including white sugar, brown sugar, powdered sugar, corn syrup, maple syrup, honey and molasses and any foods that have refined sugar in them. **People eat too much of these and should stop eating them!** Eating these can cause weight gain leading to obesity, diabetes, insulin resistance, feed cancer cells, cause mood and energy swings and increase the risk of heart disease.

People Become Falling Stars by eating too many **starches** – including white bread, rolls, bread sticks, pizza crust, spaghetti, macaroni, lasagna noodles, egg noodles, pretzels, potato chips, cheese curls, corn chips, crackers and other foods with flour, and white rice. Some vegetables such as potatoes and corn, and some fruits such as pears and bananas are very high in carbs.

To be healthy now and as you get older, you must exercise and make healthy food choices. The section content pages of this book provide good choices for healthy snacks for you to make and eat. The facing pages of **Falling Stars** are foods your body doesn't need.

Easy
Low Carb Creations
for kids

Dairy, Nuts and Seeds

Dairy products are excellent sources of needed vitamins, minerals, and protein. Utilize the following carbohydrate counts to make informed choices. A serving size is 8 ounces unless otherwise noted.

Half-and-half	8
Heavy cream, liquid	0
Nonfat milk, skim	13
Reduced fat milk, 2% milk fat	12
Sour cream (2 T. = 2)	16
Whole milk	12
Yogurt, plain whole milk	11

Cheese provides benefits of other dairy products in a compact package. Serving sizes are 1-ounce for hard cheese (makes about 1/4 cup grated) and 2 tablespoons for soft cheese.

American(1 slice, 3/4-ounce = .7)	1
Cheddar	0
Cottage, 4% milk fat, 1/2 cup	4
Cream, plain	2
Mozzarella, part skim	0
Mozzarella, whole milk	1
Parmesan, grated, 1 tablespoon	0
Swiss	1

Nuts and seeds provide a great snack and add flavor and crunch to many recipes. Being high in protein, fiber and fat, they are nutrient rich. Listed below are the net carbs per serving. A serving size measures 1/4 cup nuts or seeds unless otherwise noted.

Almonds, sliced or slivered	2
Almonds, whole, roasted	3
Cashews, whole, roasted	6
Coconut, dried, shredded, sweetened	5
Peanut butter, 2 tablespoons	5
Peanuts, dry-roasted	4
Peanuts, oil-roasted	4
Pecans	2
Pistachios	6
Pumpkin seeds, hulled	11
Sesame seeds, 2 tablespoons	0
Sunflower seeds, hulled	6
Walnuts	0

Easy
Low Carb Creations
for kids

Fruits and Vegetables

Fresh fruits are recommended for vitamins, fiber and the fact that no refined sugar has been added. Serving size is 1/2 cup fresh or frozen unless otherwise noted.

The following fruits contain fewer than 6 net carbs per serving.

Avocado, 1/2 of fruit
Blackberries
Cherries, sour

Plum, 1 fruit
Raspberries

Strawberries
Watermelon

The following fruits have 6-10 net carbs per serving.

Apple, 1/2 medium
Apricots, 3 whole
Blueberries
Cantaloupe

Cherries, sweet
Grapefruit
Honeydew melon
Kiwifruit

Orange sections
Peach, 1 small
Pineapple chunks
Tangerine, 1 small

The following fruits have 11-15 net carbs per serving and should be eaten sparingly.

Green seedless grapes
Nectarine, 1 medium

Red seedless grapes
Whole orange, 1 medium

Bananas and pears have more than 15 net carbs per small fruit.

Vegetables are filled with vitamins, minerals and antioxidants. Serving size is 1/2 cup fresh, frozen or canned unless otherwise noted.

The following vegetables, all have fewer than 4 net carbs per serving.

Asparagus
Broccoli
Cabbage
Cauliflower
Celery

Cucumber
Green beans
Green onions
Green pepper
Lettuce

Mushrooms
Spinach
Tomato
Zucchini

The following vegetables have 4-8 carbs per serving.

"California Blend"
Carrots,
Cherry tomatoes

Onion
Peas, frozen

The following vegetables have more than 8 carbs per serving and should be eaten sparingly.

Corn, 1/2 cup or 1 cob
Potatoes
Sweet potatoes

WHAT IF?

Star Light, **Star** Bright, What Low Carb Snack Will I Eat Tonight?

Stars practice before their big event. Before a theatre production or ballet, **Stars** have a dress rehearsal. Before a concert, **Stars** practice and do sound and lighting checks. Before a sporting event, **Stars** have a practice in the field, on the diamond, or in the gym in which they will be competing to check the lighting, and *feel* of the place they will perform. To be a **Star**, you must also be prepared and think of your game plan before going out with friends and family. You must ask yourself, "What foods will there be at this event? Will there be any low carb foods or do I need to pack my own?" Some foods can be eaten in a way that reduces the carb content; others should just not be eaten. Sometimes taking a snack with you is your best track to **Stardom**...

Star Suggestions:

A Big Mac® Sandwich...remove 2 of the bun pieces and eat with a fork to be a **Star**...
★   Be a **Super Star** and remove all 3 bun pieces.

Taco Salad...don't eat the shell to be a **Star**...
★   Be a **Super Star** and don't eat the beans either.

Chicken Fajitas...don't eat the fajita shells or rice to be a **Star**...
★   Be a **Super Star** and don't eat the beans either.

Pizza...place toppings from 2 pieces of pizza on top of another piece to be a **Star**...
★   Be a **Super Star** and don't eat any crust.

Salads...order regular dressing instead of fat free to be a **Star**...
★   Be a **Super Star** and don't eat the croutons.

Sausage Egg Cheese Biscuit...eat only the bottom biscuit with topping to be a **Star**...
★   Be a **Super Star** and only eat the sausage, egg and cheese.

Sausage Gravy and Biscuits...eat only a small half of biscuit with gravy to be a **Star**...
★   Be a **Super Star** and eat only the gravy over scrambled or fried eggs.

Easy **Low Carb Creations**
for kids

BE A STAR...

At the movies...

★ Take a baggie of Savory Mix...Skip the popcorn
★ Take a baggie of Spiced Almonds...Skip the candy
★ If drinking soda pop...Make sure it's diet, no sugar added
★ Be a **Super Star** and drink bottled water...Skip the soda pop

At a birthday party...

★ Eat a small piece of cake or ice cream...not both
★ Scrape off the frosting from the cake...
★ Put no toppings except nuts on the ice cream...
★ Be a **Super Star** and take 2 Chocolate Brownie Meringues to eat
★ Skip the ice cream and cake...drink milk or water

At a buffet...

★ Eat tossed salad or Ceasar salad...Skip the pickled beets and jello
★ Eat meat, chicken, fish...Skip the spaghetti and nachos
★ Eat green beans, broccoli, cauliflower with cheese sauce...
★ Skip the mashed potatoes, french fries and dinner rolls
★ Be a **Super Star** and skip dessert...drink milk or water

Easy **Low Carb Creations** for kids

STAR...TING LINE UP

★ Clean clothes
★ Hair tied back
★ Clean hands and fingernails
★ Clean countertops
★ Clean utensils, equipment, pots and pans
★ Remember, if you touch your face, hair, go to the bathroom, sneeze, cough or blow your nose, you must wash your hands.

STAR...RING FOOD SANITATION

★ Fresh fruits and vegetables must be rinsed well under cold running water; pat them dry with paper towels.

★ Fresh uncooked beef (not hamburger), pork (not sausage), chicken and fish (shellfish too) must be rinsed well under cold running water; pat dry with paper towels.
★ After touching raw beef, pork, poultry (this includes chicken), fish or eggs, wash hands, all equipment, utensils and countertop it touched with hot soapy water; rinse well.

STAR...RING FOOD PREPARATION TERMS

★ Beat...Use wooden spoon in a fast over-and-over motion or use an electric mixer on medium to high speed

★ Chopped...Use knife and cutting board; cut downward through food to make small pieces or use food chopper to make small pieces
★ Finely Chopped...Use food chopper or grinder to make tiny pieces (it will look like crumbs)
★ Fold-in...Use a rubber scraper in a gentle over-and-over motion to lightly combine foods
★ Mix...Use a wooden spoon in a circular motion or use an electric mixer on low speed
★ Soft Peak Stage...When using an electric mixer to beat egg whites, continue beating until mixture no longer just looks foamy

Stop beating; pull mixer beaters up out of mixture. Peaks will form but the tip of the peaks will flop over.

★ Stiff Peak Stage... Continue to beat egg white mixture with electric mixer after it reaches the soft peak stage. Stop beating; pull mixer beaters up out of mixture. Stiff peaks will stand up and not flop over.

★ Stir...Use wooden spoon in a circular motion

STAR...RING COOKING TERMS

★ Bake...Cooking food in an oven

★ Boil...Cooking liquid in a pan on top of the stove when large bubbles form and rise to the surface and break

★ Broil...Cooking foods directly below the heating element in top of oven on a broiler pan

★ Simmer...Cooking liquid in a pan on top of the stove when bubbles rise gently and just begin to break the surface

STAR...RING MEASURING EQUIPMENT

★ Individual 1/4, 1/3, 1/2 and 1 cup plastic or metal cups are used to measure dry ingredients. Use a straight-edged spatula or knife to level off flat. The same cups are used to measure gooey ingredients, such as peanut butter, using a rubber spatula to get it in and out of the cup.

★ Glass or clear plastic measuring cups are used to measure liquids. Place cup on a flat surface and fill to the line of the amount you want; be sure to look at the line at eye level.

★ Measuring spoons come in 1/4 teaspoon, 1/2 teaspoon, 1 teaspoon and 1 tablespoon (if you're lucky you may also have a 1/8 teaspoon and 1/2 tablespoon.) When measuring dry ingredients, be sure to level off flat with a straight edged spatula or knife. For measuring liquids, fill measuring spoon to the top.

Don't be a Falling Star...

Falling Stars Burn Out

Nabisco® Nutter Butter Sandwich Cookie

Keebler's® Chips Deluxe, Original Cookie

Little Debbie's® Fudge Round

9 Net Carbs

18 Net Carbs

22 Net Carbs

Easy Low Carb Creations for kids

*Star*t Now, Eat Later

Net Carbs

Cherry Almond Cheesecake Cookies 20

Chocolate Brownie Meringues 21

Coconut Macaroons. . . . 22

Lemon Meringue Cookies 23

Peanut Butter Cookies 24

Strawberry Pecan Cheese-cake Cookies . . 25

*Star*tling Facts:

1. The average American eats _____ pounds of added sugar each year.
2. Much of the sugar in foods comes from _____ syrup.
3. The sugar substitute used in these recipes is _____.

Cookie Stars

Easy **Low Carb Creations** for kids

1 Serving
2
Net Carbs
2 Protein
1 Fiber
3 Carbs

> 15

Cherry Almond Cheesecake Cookies
Makes 24 servings/1 cookie each

1 8-ounce package cream
    cheese, softened

1/4 cup Cherry Simply Fruit®
2 tablespoons Splenda®
1/4 teaspoon cinnamon
1/4 teaspoon almond extract
1/4 cup almonds, chopped

3/4 cup almonds, finely chopped

Directions
1. In medium bowl, place cream
   cheese; beat with electric
   mixer until creamy.
2. To same bowl, add next 5
   ingredients. Beat until well
   blended.
3. Freeze cookie dough 10
   minutes or until slightly firm.
4. Place finely chopped almonds
   in small bowl.
5. Roll dough into 3/4-inch balls;
   roll in chopped almonds.
6. Chill additional 20 minutes.
   For firm cookies, freeze 20
   minutes.

Easy **Low Carb Creations**
for kids

Chocolate Brownie Meringues

Makes 24 servings/1 cookie each

3 1-ounce unsweetened baking chocolate squares

2 egg whites
Dash salt
1/2 teaspoon vinegar
1/2 teaspoon vanilla

1 cup Splenda®
1 cup chopped pecans

Directions
1. Preheat oven to 350 degrees.
2. Into small microwave-safe bowl, place chocolate; cover with waxed paper. On high power level, cook chocolate 2 minutes or until melted. Stir and set aside until cool.
3. In medium bowl, combine next 4 ingredients. Beat with electric mixer until soft peaks form.
4. To egg white mixture, gradually add Splenda®, beating until stiff peaks form.
5. To same bowl, fold in chocolate and pecans.
6. Coat large baking sheet with non-stick cooking spray.
7. Onto baking sheet, drop cookie dough from a tablespoon.
8. Bake cookies 10 minutes.

1 Serving
2 Protein
2
Net Carbs
2 Carbs
1 Fiber
> 15

Easy **Low Carb Creations**
for kids

1 Serving

3 Net Carbs

1 Protein

1 Fiber

4 Carbs

> 15

Coconut Macaroons

Makes 18 servings/1 cookie each

1 1/3 cups flaked coconut
1/3 cup Splenda®
2 tablespoons flour
1/8 teaspoon salt

2 egg whites
1/2 teaspoon vanilla extract

Directions

1. Preheat oven to 325 degrees.
2. In small bowl, combine first 4 ingredients.
3. To same bowl, stir in remaining ingredients; mix well.
4. Coat baking sheet with non-stick cooking spray.
5. Drop cookie dough by rounded teaspoonfuls onto baking sheets.
6. Bake 18-20 minutes or until golden brown.
7. Cool on wire rack.

Easy **Low Carb Creations** for kids

Lemon Meringue Cookies

Makes 24 servings/1 cookie each

4 large egg whites
1/2 teaspoon salt
1/2 teaspoon cream of tartar

1 1-ounce package sugar-free
    lemon instant pudding mix
1/2 teaspoon lemon extract

1/2 cup shredded coconut
1 1/2 cups sliced almonds

Directions
1. Preheat oven to 300 degrees.
2. Coat baking sheets with non-stick cooking spray.
3. In medium bowl, add first 3 ingredients; beat with electric mixer until soft peaks form.
4. To same bowl, gradually add pudding mix and lemon extract; beating until stiff peaks form.
5. To lemon mixture, gently fold in coconut and sliced almonds, 1/2 cup at a time.
6. Drop cookie dough by level tablespoon onto baking sheet.
7. Bake 20-25 minutes or until meringues are dry and crisp.
8. Cool cookies on baking sheets 2 minutes; remove to wire racks to cool completely.

Easy **Low Carb Creations** *for kids*

1
Serving

3
Protein

1

Net Carbs

1
Fiber

2
Carbs

> 15

Peanut Butter Cookies

Makes 24 servings/1 cookie each

1 egg

1 cup peanut butter
3/4 cup plus 2 tablespoons
     Splenda®
1 teaspoon vanilla

Directions

1. Preheat oven to 350 degrees.
2. In medium bowl, beat egg slightly.
3. Add remaining ingredients; mix well.
4. Shape into teaspoon-sized balls; place 2 inches apart on baking sheet; flatten with fork.
5. Bake 16 to18 minutes or until set.
6. Cool 5 minutes; remove to cooling racks.

Strawberry Pecan Cheesecake Cookies

Makes 24 servings/1 cookie each

1 8-ounce package cream
    cheese, softened

1/4 cup sugar-free strawberry
    preserves
2 tablespoons Splenda®
1/4 teaspoon cinnamon
1/4 teaspoon vanilla extract
1/4 cup pecan pieces

3/4 cup pecans, finely chopped

Directions

1. In medium bowl, place cream
   cheese; beat with electric
   mixer until creamy.
2. To same bowl, add next 5
   ingredients. Beat until well
   blended.
3. Freeze cookie dough 10
   minutes or until slightly firm.
4. Place finely chopped pecans
   in small bowl.
5. Roll dough into 3/4-inch balls;
   roll in chopped pecans.
6. Chill additional 20 minutes.
   For firm cookies, freeze 20
   minutes.

Easy Low Carb Creations
for kids

Don't be a Falling Star...

Start Now, Eat Later

Net Carbs

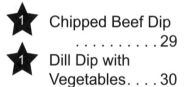

1   Chipped Beef Dip
. . . . 29

1   Dill Dip with Vegetables 30

I'm Starving

Net Carbs

1   Cheese Dip with Vegetables 28

2   Fruity Fruit Dip
. . . . 31

Dipping Stars

Easy **Low Carb Creations** *for kids*

Cheese Dip with Vegetables

Makes 14 servings/2 tablespoons each

1 8-ounce package cream
  cheese, softened
2 tablespoons butter, softened
1/8 teaspoon onion salt
1/8 teaspoon garlic salt
1 5-ounce jar pasteurized process
  cheese spread, Old
  English Style®

cauliflower, broccoli and
carrots.

Directions
1. In medium bowl, place all
   ingredients; beat with electric
   mixer until smooth.
2. Cover and chill.
3. Serve with fresh sliced
   cucumbers, celery sticks,

Chipped Beef Dip

Makes 20 servings/2 tablespoons each

1 8-ounce package cream
    cheese, softened

1 8-ounce carton sour cream

1 2.25-ounce package chipped
    beef, finely chopped
1 teaspoon Ranch salad dressing
    mix

Directions
1. In medium bowl, place cream cheese. Beat with electric mixer until smooth.
2. To cream cheese, add sour cream; beat until smooth.
3. To same bowl, add remaining ingredients; mix until well blended. Chill 1 hour.
4. Serve with fresh sliced cucumbers, celery sticks, cauliflower, broccoli and carrots.

1 Serving
Protein 2
1 Net Carbs
Carbs 1
Fiber 0
> 15

Easy **Low Carb Creations**
for kids

Dill Dip with Vegetables

Makes 17 servings/2 tablespoons each

1 cup mayonnaise
1 cup sour cream
2 tablespoons dill weed
1 teaspoon garlic salt
1/2 teaspoon onion powder

Directions
1. In medium bowl, combine all ingredients; stir well.
2. Cover and chill at least 2 hours.
3. Serve with fresh sliced cucumbers, celery sticks, cauliflower, broccoli and carrots.

Easy **Low Carb Creations** *for kids*

Fruity Fruit Dip

Makes 16 servings/2 tablespoons each

1 8-ounce package cream
   cheese, softened

1 cup sour cream
1 .3-ounce package sugar-free
   strawberry gelatin
1 tablespoon lemon juice
2 tablespoons Splenda®

Directions

1. In medium bowl, place cream
   cheese; beat with electric
   mixer until creamy.
2. To same bowl, add remaining
   ingredients; beat until creamy
   and well blended.
3. Cover bowl and chill.
4. Serve Fruity Fruit Dip
   with strawberries, orange
   segments or apple slices (put
   apples in lemon juice or Diet
   7-Up® to slow browning).

1 Serving
2 Protein
2 Net Carbs
2 Carbs
0 Fiber
< 15

Don't be a Falling Star...

Falling Stars Burn Out

Dairy Queen® Banana Split

93 Net Carbs

Ben and Jerry's® Chunky Monkey Ice Cream 1/2 cup

29 Net Carbs

Orange Push-Up

18 Net Carbs

Easy Low Carb Creations for kids

Start Now, Eat Later

Net Carbs

10 Banana Split Dessert 34

4 Chocolate White Chocolate Pops 35

9 Cranberry, Strawberry Yogurt Pops 36

10 Creamy Orange Yogurt Pops . . . 37

0 Frozen Pops 38

2 Vanilla Ice Cream 39

Startling Facts:

1. The average American eats _____ pounds of ice cream each. **Sugar-free ice cream is great.**
2. The average American drinks _____ gallons of soda pop each year. **Water is better for you!**

Answers: 1. 22; 2. 50

Frozen Stars

Easy **Low Carb Creations** for kids

Banana Split Dessert

Makes 18 servings

1
Serving

10

Net Carbs

1
Protein

11
Carbs

1
Fiber

> 15

1 1-ounce package sugar-free banana instant pudding mix
2 cups half-and-half

1 1-ounce package sugar-free chocolate instant pudding mix
1 1/2 cups half-and-half

1 8-ounce carton whipped topping

1/4 teaspoon pineapple extract

1/2 cup chopped peanuts
2 tablespoons chocolate sprinkles

Directions

1. In medium bowl, combine first 2 ingredients. Prepare pudding according to package directions.

2. Into 9 x 13-inch glass pan, pour pudding mixture. Place in freezer until firm.

3. In medium bowl, add next 2 ingredients. Prepare pudding according to package directions.

4. Into chocolate pudding, fold 1/2 cup whipped topping.

5. Onto frozen banana pudding, pour chocolate pudding layer. Return to freezer until firm.

6. Into remaining whipped topping, stir 1/4 teaspoon pineapple extract.

7. Onto frozen chocolate pudding layer, spread flavored whipped topping.

8. On top of dessert, evenly sprinkle chopped nuts and chocolate sprinkles.

Chocolate White Chocolate Pops
Makes 10 servings

1 1-ounce package sugar-free
    white chocolate instant
    pudding mix
2 tablespoons sugar-free
    Nesquik®
3 cups milk

10 3-ounce paper cups
10 popsicle sticks
10 4-inch squares of aluminum
    foil

Directions
1. Into medium bowl, combine all ingredients: beat with electric mixer 2 minutes.
2. Into paper cups, pour chocolate pudding mixture.
3. Cut a slit in the middle of each foil piece and cover cups.
4. Place popsicle stick in the foil slit for each cup.
5. Freeze 4 hours or until firm.
6. Remove cups to serve pops.

1 Serving
3 Protein
4
Net Carbs
4 Carbs
0 Fiber

> 15

Easy Low Carb Creations
for kids

Cranberry, Strawberry Yogurt Pops
Makes 10 servings

2 8-ounce cartons lite strawberry
    yogurt
2 cups cranberry juice

10 3-ounce paper cups
10 popsicle sticks
10 4-inch squares of aluminum foil

Directions
1. Into 2-quart pitcher, place strawberry yogurt and cranberry juice. Use long wooden spoon and mix well. (If you know how to use an electric blender, blend on high 2 minutes.)
2. Into paper cups, pour cranberry/strawberry mixture.
3. Cut a slit in the middle of each foil piece and cover cups.
4. Place popsicle stick in the foil slit for each cup.
5. Freeze 4 hours or until firm.
6. Remove cups to serve pops.

1 Serving
2 Protein
9
Net Carbs
0 Fiber
9 Carbs

> 15

Easy
Low Carb Creations
for kids

Creamy Orange Yogurt Pops
Makes 10 servings

2 8-ounce cartons lite orange
    yogurt
2 cups orange juice

10 3-ounce paper cups
10 popsicle sticks
10 4-inch squares of aluminum
    foil

Directions
1. Into 2-quart pitcher, place orange yogurt and orange juice. Use long wooden spoon and mix well. (If you know how to use an electric blender, blend on high 2 minutes.)
2. Into paper cups, pour yogurt/juice mixture.
3. Cut a slit in the middle of each foil piece and cover cups.
4. Place popsicle stick in the foil slit for each cup.
5. Freeze 4 hours or until firm.
6. Remove cups to serve pops.

1
Serving
2
Protein
10
Net Carbs
10
Carbs
0
Fiber

> 15

Easy
Low Carb Creations
for kids

Frozen Pops
Makes 8 servings

1 .3-ounce package sugar-free gelatin (any flavor)
1 small package sugar-free drink mix (any flavor)
2 cups boiling water

2 cups cold water

8 5-ounce paper cups
8 popsicle sticks
8 4-inch squares aluminum foil

Directions
1. In large bowl, mix first three ingredients together until dissolved.
2. Stir in 2 cups cold water.
3. Pour into popsicle holders or fill paper cups 3/4 full.
4. Cut a slit in the middle of each foil piece and cover cups.
5. Place popsicle stick in each cup.
6. Freeze 4 hours or until firm.
7. Remove cups to serve frozen pops.

0
Serving

0
Protein

0

Net Carbs

0
Fiber

0
Carbs

15

Easy Low Carb Creations for kids

Vanilla Ice Cream

Makes 22 servings

5 eggs

1 quart whole milk
3 cups Splenda®

3 tablespoons vanilla extract
7 cups heavy whipping cream

22 snack-size sealable plastic
    bags
22 1/2 gallon sealable plastic
    bags
1 large bag ice
1 1/2 cups salt

Directions

1. In medium saucepan, place eggs; beat slightly.
2. To same pan, add next 2 ingredients; over medium-low heat, cook 12 minutes until mixture slightly thickens and coats wooden spoon.
3. Remove saucepan from stove; set aside until mixture is room temperature.
4. Place mixture in refrigerator; chill 1 hour or more.
5. To chilled mixture, add next 2 ingredients. Stir well.
6. Place 1/2 cup liquid in each snack-size bag and seal tightly.
7. Into 1/2 gallon bags place 4 cups of ice, 1 tablespoon salt and snack-size bag with cream mixture.
8. Shake bag with ice and cream mixture 10 minutes.

Note: This recipe works well in a 1 gallon ice cream freezer.

1 Serving

2 Protein

2

Net Carbs

2 Carbs

0 Fiber

> 15

Easy **Low Carb Creations**
for kids

Don't be a Falling Star...

Falling Stars Burn Out

Starbuck's® Mocha Frappuccino Grande

58 Net Carbs

Coke® 12 oz can

38 Net Carbs

Kiwi Strawberry Snapple® 20 oz bottle

70 Net Carbs

Easy **Low Carb Creations** for kids

*Star*t Now, Eat Later

Net Carbs

 Lemon Shake-ups . . . 43

I'm *Star*ving

Net Carbs

⭐ 6 Berry Smoothie 42
⭐ 4 Orange Julius 44
⭐ 3 Peach Coolers 45

Liquid Stars

Easy **Low Carb Creations** for kids

Berry Smoothie
Makes 6 servings/6 ounces each

1 1/4 cups milk
1 1/4 cups fresh or frozen
    (unsweetened)
    strawberries
1/2 cup fresh or frozen
    (unsweetened) raspberries
3 tablespoons Splenda®
1 1/2 cups ice cubes

Directions
1.   Into blender, pour all
    ingredients; cover with lid.
2.   Blend on high 1-2 minutes or
    until smooth.

< 15

1
Serving
6
Net Carbs
2
Protein
1
Fiber
7
Carbs

Lemon Shake-ups

Makes 6 servings/16 ounces each

1 cup water
1 cup Splenda®

7 large lemons

4 cups water

12 cups ice

Directions

1. Into small saucepan, place first 2 ingredients. Over medium-high heat, cook and stir until mixture boils.
2. Remove saucepan from stove; set aside until mixture is room temperature.
3. Place mixture in refrigerator; cool completely.
4. Meanwhile, squeeze juice from 6 lemons; remove and throw away seeds.
5. Cut remaining lemon into small pieces; set aside.
6. Into pitcher, pour mixture and juice; stir well.
7. To same pitcher, add 4 cups cold water and stir.
8. To serve, into 16-ounce cup place 2 cups ice, 1 to 2 lemon pieces and fill cup with lemon mixture.

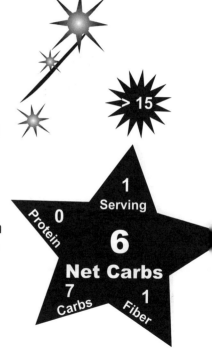

> 15

1 Serving

Protein 0

6
Net Carbs

7 Carbs

1 Fiber

Easy **Low Carb Creations** for kids

Orange Julius
Makes 6 servings/6 ounces each

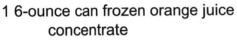

1 6-ounce can frozen orange juice
concentrate
1 cup milk
1/2 cup water
1/4 cup Splenda®
2 teaspoons vanilla
2 1/4 cups ice cubes

< 15

1
Serving
4
Net Carbs
1 Protein
4 Carbs
0 Fiber

Directions
1. Into blender, pour all ingredients; cover with lid.
2. Blend on high 1-2 minutes or until smooth.

Peach Coolers
Makes 8 servings/6 ounces each

1/4 cup lemon juice
6 packets Sweet-N-Low®
2 large ripe peaches, peeled,
      seed removed
2 cups Diet 7-Up®
2 cups ice cubes

Directions
1. Into blender, pour all
   ingredients; cover with lid.
2. Blend on high 1-2 minutes or
   until smooth.

< 15

1 Serving

Protein 0

3
Net Carbs

3 Carbs

0 Fiber

Easy Low Carb Creations
for kids

Don't be a Falling Star...

Falling Stars Burn Out

Papa John's® Pepperoni Pizza 1/8 of 14"

37 Net Carbs

Subway's® Tuna Deli Style Sandwich

33 Net Carbs

Big Mac®

46 Net Carbs

Big Mac® without bun is 9 net carbs

Easy Low Carb Creations for kids

Start Now, Eat Later

Net Carbs **> 15**

7 Bacon Tomato Stars 48

2 B.B.Q. Wings 49

1 Broccoli Cheese Ham Roll-ups. . 50

1 Chicken Drumettes 51

1 Ham and Cheese Cups 52

9 Layered Tex-Mex Bowls. 55

6 Sweet and Sour Dogs 58

6 Tex-Mex Dogs 59

7 Tuna Salad Canoes 60

I'm Starving

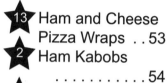

Net Carbs **< 15**

13 Ham and Cheese Pizza Wraps . . 53

2 Ham Kabobs 54

12 Pepperoni Pizza Wraps 56

4 Sausage Kabobs 57

7 Turkey Kabobs 61

Meal Making Stars

1 Serving

7

10 Protein

Net Carbs

1 Fiber

8 Carbs

15

Bacon Tomato Stars

Makes 6 servings

4 eggs

1 pound bacon, cut into 1/2-inch pieces

2 tablespoons green onion

1 cup lettuce, chopped
1/2 cup Miracle Whip®

6 large tomatoes
1/2 teaspoon salt

Directions

1. In small saucepan, place eggs and cover with water to 1-inch above eggs. Bring water to boil. Boil 5 minutes. Cover, remove from heat; let sit 20 minutes. Pour off hot water; cover eggs with cold water to cool.

2. Meanwhile, in skillet over medium-high heat, cook bacon until crisp; drain onto paper towels.

3. With food chopper, chop bacon and green onions until very finely chopped.

4. In medium bowl, combine bacon, onion and next 2 ingredients.

5. After eggs have cooled, peel hard shell from eggs; chop eggs.

6. To bowl with bacon mixture, add chopped eggs. Stir until ingredients are well blended. Chill.

7. Wash tomatoes; remove stem.

8. Turn tomatoes stem side down; cut each one not quite through in 6 equal sections.

9. Spread tomatoes apart; sprinkle with salt.

10. Fill each tomato with bacon mixture. Chill.

B.B.Q. Wings

Makes 20 servings/2 pieces each

1 16-ounce bottle ketchup
3/4 cup Splenda®
3 tablespoons Worcestershire
    sauce
1 tablespoon cider vinegar
2 tablespoons mustard
1/2 cup dill pickle juice
2 tablespoons onion, finely
    chopped

40 chicken wings (5 pound bag)

Directions

1. In medium saucepan, combine first 7 ingredients. Over medium heat, cook and stir; bring to boil.
2. Remove saucepan from stove; set aside until mixture is room temperature.
3. To large bowl, add chicken.
4. Cover chicken with B.B.Q. Sauce and chill 4 hours, turning several times.
5. Preheat oven to 375 degrees.
6. On foil-lined sheet cake pan, place chicken. Save B.B.Q. Sauce.
7. Bake 30 minutes; brush with saved B.B.Q. Sauce.
8. Turn chicken; brush with B.B.Q. Sauce and bake additional 30 minutes.
9. Throw away remaining B.B.Q. Sauce. Do NOT use it for a dipping sauce.

49

1 Serving

9 Protein

2
Net Carbs

2 Carbs

0 Fiber

> 15

1 Serving
1 Net Carbs
16 Protein
2 Carbs
1 Fiber

> 15

Broccoli, Cheese, Ham Roll-Ups
Makes 6 servings

1 10-ounce package frozen broccoli spears

2 2.5-ounce packages thin sliced smoked ham

6 slices American cheese

Directions

1. In microwave oven-safe bowl, cook broccoli in microwave oven according to package directions.
2. Drain broccoli; place on paper towel to dry. Divide into 6 equal portions.
3. Place 3 ham slices on top of one another so about 3/4 of the circle overlaps on each one.
4. On top of ham slices, place cheese slice and broccoli spears.
5. Roll ham up like a Fruit Roll Up®; secure with toothpick.
6. In microwave safe dish, place ham rolls.
7. In microwave oven on medium power, heat ham roll-ups 4 minutes or until cheese melts.

Chicken Drumettes
Makes 20 servings/2 pieces each

1/2 cup lemon juice
1/2 cup vegetable oil
3/4 teaspoons ginger
1/2 cup ketchup
1/2 cup soy sauce
1/4 teaspoon garlic powder

40 chicken drumettes (5 pound bag)

Directions
1. In large bowl, combine first 6 ingredients to make marinade. Mix well.
2. To same bowl, add chicken; stir to coat with marinade. Cover and chill at least 4 hours or overnight, turning several times.
3. Preheat oven to 375 degrees.
4. In foil-lined sheet cake pan, place chicken. Save marinade.
5. Bake 30 minutes; brush with saved marinade.
6. Turn chicken; brush with marinade and bake additional 30 minutes.
7. Throw away remaining marinade. Do NOT use it for a dipping sauce.

1 Serving
Protein 10
1
Net Carbs
1 Carbs
0 Fiber

> 15

1 Serving

1 Net Carbs

13 Protein

0 Fiber

1 Carbs

> 15

Ham and Cheese Cups

Makes 6 servings

1 2.5-ounce package thin sliced
    smoked ham

4 eggs

2 tablespoons milk
1/4 cup green pepper, chopped
1/4 teaspoon mustard
1 cup shredded Monterey Jack
    cheese
1/8 teaspoon salt
1 dash pepper

Directions
1. Preheat oven to 350 degrees.
2. Coat muffin pan with non-stick cooking spray.
3. Into muffin pan, press 2 pieces of ham into each of the 6 cups.
4. In medium bowl, slightly beat eggs.
5. To same bowl, stir in remaining ingredients.
6. Pour egg mixture evenly into ham cups.
7. Bake 20-25 minutes or until knife inserted near center comes out clean.

Ham and Cheese Pizza Wraps

Makes 1 serving

1 Serving
26 Protein
13
Net Carbs
15 Carbs
2 Fiber

< 15

1 5-inch soft corn tortilla shell
2 tablespoons pizza sauce

1 tablespoon canned
     mushrooms, drained
5 thin slices smoked ham, torn
     into bite-sized pieces
1/4 cup mozzarella cheese

Paper towel

Directions

1. Onto center of tortilla shell, spread pizza sauce in a 2-inch strip from top of shell to the bottom.
2. Onto sauce, place next 3 ingredients in order given.
3. Fold left side of tortilla shell over fillings. Fold right side over it.
4. Onto paper towel, place filled tortilla wrap. Roll up tortilla wrap in paper towel.
5. In microwave oven on medium power, heat pizza wrap 1 minute or until cheese melts.

Easy **Low Carb Creations**
for kids

1 Serving

2

Net Carbs

57 Protein

0 Fiber

2 Carbs

< 15

Ham Kabobs

Makes 4 servings/3 Kabobs each

2 1/2-inch thick slices cooked
      ham, cut into 24 cubes
12 1/2-inch cubes Swiss cheese
12 stuffed green olives
12 toothpicks

Directions
1. On each toothpick, place 1
    ham cube, 1 cheese cube, 1
    olive and another ham cube.

Easy
Low Carb Creations
for kids

Layered Tex-Mex Bowls

Makes 12 servings

3 ripe avocados, chopped
1/2 cup onion, chopped and
    divided
3 large tomatoes, chopped and
    divided

1 pound lean ground beef
1 package taco seasoning mix

1 16-ounce can refried beans

1/2 head lettuce, shredded
1 tomato, chopped

1 8-ounce package tortilla chips
1 cup sour cream
2 cups shredded cheddar cheese
1 7-ounce can sliced black olives,
    drained

Directions

1. In medium bowl, combine avocados, 1/4 cup onion and 1/2 cup tomatoes; mix well.
2. In skillet, cook ground beef with remaining 1/4 cup onion, stirring until meat is brown and crumbly; drain.
3. Add taco seasoning packet; follow packet directions.
4. Add refried beans to meat mixture, continue cooking 1 to 2 minutes or until beans are hot.
5. In medium bowl, toss lettuce with remaining chopped tomato.
6. In individual bowls, layer ingredients in the following order; tortilla chips, avocado mixture, sour cream, ground beef mixture, lettuce mixture, cheese and black olives.

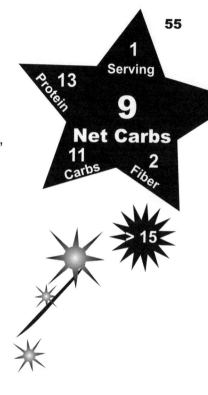

1 Serving
13 Protein
9 Net Carbs
11 Carbs
2 Fiber

> 15

Easy **Low Carb Creations**
for kids

1
Serving

27
Protein

12

Net Carbs

2
Fiber

14
Carbs

< 15

Pepperoni Pizza Wraps
Makes 1 serving

1 5-inch soft corn tortilla shell
2 tablespoons pizza sauce

1 tablespoon canned mushrooms,
    drained
10 small round slices pepperoni
1/4 cup shredded mozzarella
    cheese

Paper towel

Directions
1. Onto center of tortilla shell, spread pizza sauce in a 2-inch strip from top of shell to the bottom.
2. Onto sauce, place next 3 ingredients in order given.
3. Fold left side of tortilla shell over fillings. Fold right side over it.
4. Onto paper towel, place filled tortilla wrap. Roll up tortilla wrap in paper towel.
5. In microwave oven on medium power, heat pizza wrap 1 minute or until cheese melts.

Sausage Kabobs

Makes 5 servings/3 Kabobs each

1 package Smoky Link Sausages®, cut sausage links into thirds

15 1/2-inch cubes cheddar cheese
1 12-ounce can pineapple chunks, drained
15 toothpicks

Directions

1. In small skillet, place sausage pieces. Over medium-high heat, cook and stir sausage pieces 5 minutes or until brown.
2. On each toothpick, place 1 piece sausage, 1 cheese cube, 1 pineapple chunk and another sausage piece.

1 Serving
Protein 16
4
Net Carbs
4 Carbs
0 Fiber

< 15

Easy **Low Carb Creations** for kids

1
Serving

5
Protein

6

Net Carbs

0
Fiber

6
Carbs

> 15

Sweet and Sour Dogs

Makes 20 servings/approximately 5 pieces each

1 tablespoon cornstarch
1/2 cup Splenda®

1 8-ounce can tomato sauce
1 cup pineapple juice
1/3 cup vinegar

2 pounds beef hot dogs, cut into
        1-inch pieces

Directions
1. In medium saucepan, combine cornstarch and Splenda®.
2. To same pan, stir in next 3 ingredients. Over medium heat, cook and stir until mixture boils.
3. To tomato sauce mixture, add hot dog pieces. Bring mixture to boil.
4. Reduce heat to medium and simmer 15 minutes, stirring occasionally.

Easy **Low Carb Creations**
for kids

Tex-Mex Dogs

Makes 10 servings

1 cup finely shredded cheddar
    cheese
1/2 cup tortilla chips, crushed
2 green onions, thinly sliced
3 tablespoons salsa
2 tablespoons mayonnaise
1/2 teaspoon chili powder

10 beef hot dogs

Directions
1. Turn oven to broil/high.
2. In medium bowl, combine first 6 ingredients.
3. Cut a 1/2-inch deep lengthwise slit in each hot dog.
4. Into each hot dog, spoon 2 tablespoons cheese mixture.
5. Coat broiler pan with non-stick cooking spray.
6. Onto broiler pan, place stuffed hot dogs.
7. Broil 3 minutes or until cheese melts.

1 Serving

Protein 9

6
Net Carbs

Carbs 6

Fiber 0

< 15

Easy **Low Carb Creations**
for kids

1 Serving

7

Net Carbs

4 Protein

0 Fiber

7 Carbs

> 15

Tuna Salad Canoes

Makes 10 servings

4 eggs

1 12-ounce can tuna packed in
      water, drained
dash salt
dash pepper
2 teaspoons Splenda®
1/4 teaspoon vinegar
2/3 cup celery, chopped
2 tablespoons sweet pickle relish
1/2 cup Miracle Whip®

5 medium cucumbers

Directions

1. In small saucepan, place eggs and cover with water to 1-inch above eggs. Bring water to boil. Boil 5 minutes. Cover, remove from heat; let sit 20 minutes. Pour off hot water; cover eggs with cold water to cool.
2. Meanwhile, in medium bowl, combine next 8 ingredients.
3. After eggs have cooled, peel hard shell from eggs; chop eggs.
4. To bowl with tuna mixture, add chopped eggs. Stir until ingredients are well blended.
5. Cover and chill tuna salad 1 hour.
6. Wash cucumbers and peel if desired; cut cucumbers in half lengthwise. Using a spoon, remove seeded middle to make a lengthwise shell from each cucumber half.
7. Fill cucumber "Canoes" with tuna salad mixture.

Easy **Low Carb Creations** *for kids*

Turkey Kabobs

Makes 4 servings/3 Kabobs each

2 1/2-inch thick slices cooked
    turkey, cut into 24
    cubes
12 1/2-inch cubes Colby/jack
    cheese
12 green grapes
12 toothpicks

Directions
1. On each toothpick, place
   1 turkey cube, 1 cheese
   cube, 1 grape and
   another turkey cube.

Easy **Low Carb Creations**
for kids

Don't be a Falling Star...

Falling Stars Burn Out

Sour Cream
and Onion
Pringles®
1 oz serving

14
Net Carbs

Doritos®
Nacho
Cheesier
1 oz serving

16
Net Carbs

Chex
Mix
1 cup
serving

31
Net Carbs

Easy
Low Carb Creations
for kids

Start Now, Eat Later

15

Net Carbs

5 Cheddar Almonds
. . . . 64

2 Cheddar Bacon
Almonds 65

1 Cheddar Bacon
Pork Rinds 66

2 Chedder Pork
Rinds   67

5 Ranch Almonds
. . . . 70

2 Ranch Pork
Rinds 71

2 Savory Almonds
. . . . 72

13 Savory Mix
. . . . 73

I'm Starving

< 15

Net Carbs

3 Dill Pickle Canoes
. . . . 68

2 Dill Pickle Sailboats
. . . . 69

Salty Crunchy Stars

Easy **Low Carb Creations**
for kids

1 Serving

5 Net Carbs

7 Protein

3 Fiber

8 Carbs

> 15

Cheddar Almonds

Makes 12 servings/approximately 1/4 cup each

2 tablespoons butter, melted
1 12-ounce package whole
    almonds

1/4 cup plus 2 tablespoons dried
    cheddar cheese powder

Directions

1. Preheat oven to 300 degrees.
2. In medium bowl, toss together butter and almonds.
3. On top of almonds, sprinkle 1/4 cup dried cheddar cheese powder; stir well.
4. Coat 9 x 13-inch pan with non-stick cooking spray.
5. Into pan, spread almond mixture evenly.
6. Bake 30 minutes, stirring every 15 minutes.
7. Remove almonds from oven; sprinkle with 2 tablespoons dried cheddar cheese powder; stir well.
8. Serve warm or cool completely.

Easy **Low Carb Creations** for kids

Cheddar Bacon Almonds

Makes 12 servings/approximately 1/4 cup each

1/2 pound bacon, cut into 1/2-inch pieces

1 12-ounce package whole almonds

1 cup finely shredded cheddar cheese

Directions

1. Preheat oven to 300 degrees.
2. In skillet over medium-high heat, cook bacon until crisp; drain. Use food chopper to chop bacon; set aside.
3. Coat 9 x 13-inch pan with non-stick cooking spray.
4. Into pan, spread almonds evenly.
5. On top of almonds, sprinkle bacon evenly.
6. On top of bacon, sprinkle cheese evenly.
7. Bake 15 minutes or until cheese melts.
8. Serve immediately.

Cheddar Bacon Pork Rinds

Makes 8 servings/approximately 1 cup each

1
Serving

16 Protein

1
Net Carbs

0
Fiber

1
Carbs

> 15

1/2 pound bacon, cut into 1/2-inch pieces

1 5-ounce package pork rinds
1 cup finely shredded cheddar cheese

Directions
1. Preheat oven to 250 degrees.
2. In skillet over medium-high heat, cook bacon until crisp; drain. Use food chopper to chop bacon; set aside.
3. Coat 9 x 13-inch pan with non-stick cooking spray.
4. Into pan, spread pork rinds evenly.
5. On top of pork rinds, sprinkle bacon evenly.
6. On top of bacon, sprinkle cheese evenly.
7. Bake 15 minutes or until cheese melts.
8. Serve immediately.

Easy
Low Carb Creations
for kids

Cheddar Pork Rinds

Makes 8 servings/approximately 1 cup each

1 5-ounce package pork rinds
1/4 cup plus 2 tablespoons dried
    cheddar cheese powder

Directions
1. Preheat oven to 250 degrees.
2. In large bowl place pork rinds; sprinkle with 1/4 cup dried cheddar cheese powder; stir well.
3. Coat sheet cake pan with non-stick cooking spray.
4. Onto pan, spread pork rind mixture evenly.
5. Bake 30 minutes, stirring every 15 minutes.
6. Remove pork rinds from oven; sprinkle with 2 tablespoons dried cheddar cheese powder; stir well.
7. Serve warm or cool completely.

1 Serving
Protein 10
2
Net Carbs
2 Carbs
Fiber 0

> 15

Easy Low Carb Creations
for kids

Dill Pickle Canoes

Makes 10 servings/2 Canoes each

1
Serving

3
Protein

3
Net Carbs

0
Fiber

3
Carbs

< 15

1 16-ounce jar baby dill pickles, drained

4 ounces cream cheese, softened
1 2.5-ounce package smoked ham, finely chopped

Directions

1. On paper towels, place pickles to dry.
2. Cut pickles in half lengthwise. Using a spoon, remove seeded middle to make a lengthwise shell from each pickle half.
3. In medium bowl, place cream cheese and ham; beat with electric mixer until well blended.
4. Fill pickle "Canoes" with cream cheese/ham mixture. Chill.

Dill Pickle Sailboats

Makes 10 servings/2 Sailboats each

1 16-ounce jar baby dill pickles,
    drained

4 ounces cream cheese, softened
2 ounces thin sliced salami or
    smoked beef stick
60 toothpicks

Directions
1. On paper towels, place pickles to dry.
2. Cut pickles in half lengthwise. Using a spoon, remove seeded middle to make a lengthwise shell from each pickle half.
3. Fill pickle "Sailboats" with cream cheese.
4. Cut 60 2-inch triangles out of meat.
5. Place a toothpick in each triangle to make a sail.
6. Place 3 toothpick/meat sails into each boat.

1 Serving

Protein 9

2 Net Carbs

2 Carbs

0 Fiber

> 15

Easy **Low Carb Creations** for kids

Ranch Almonds

Makes 10 servings/approximately 1/4 cup each

2 tablespoons butter, melted
1 12-ounce package whole
  almonds
1 1-ounce packet Ranch salad
  dressing mix

Directions
1. Preheat oven to 300 degrees.
2. In medium bowl, toss together butter and almonds.
3. On top of almonds, sprinkle Ranch salad dressing packet contents; stir well.
4. Coat 9 x 13-inch pan with non-stick cooking spray.
5. Into pan, spread almond mixture evenly.
6. Bake 30 minutes, stirring every 15 minutes.
7. Serve warm or cool completely.

Easy **Low Carb Creations**
  for kids

Ranch Pork Rinds

Makes 8 servings/approximately 1 cup each

1 5-ounce package pork rinds
1 1-ounce packet Ranch salad
      dressing mix

Directions
1. Preheat oven to 250 degrees.
2. In large bowl, place pork rinds, sprinkle with Ranch salad dressing packet contents; stir well.
3. Coat sheet cake pan with non-stick cooking spray.
4. Onto pan, spread pork rind mixture evenly.
5. Bake 30 minutes, stirring every 15 minutes.
6. Serve warm or cool completely.

1 Serving

Protein 10

2 Net Carbs

2 Carbs

0 Fiber

> 15

Easy Low Carb Creations for kids

Savory Almonds

Makes 10 servings/approximately 1/4 cup each

1 tablespoon butter, melted
2 tablespoons Worcestershire
   sauce
1/2 teaspoon garlic powder
1/4 teaspoon onion salt
1/4 teaspoon seasoned salt

1 12-ounce package whole
   almonds

Directions

1. Preheat oven to 300 degrees.
2. In medium bowl, combine first
   5 ingredients.
3. To same bowl, add almonds.
   Stir well to coat until all liquid
   is absorbed.
4. Coat 9 x 13-inch pan with
   non-stick cooking spray.
5. Into pan, spread almond
   mixture evenly.
6. Bake 30 minutes, stirring
   every 15 minutes.
7. Serve warm or cool
   completely.

Savory Mix

Makes 12 servings/approximately 1 cup each

1 tablespoon butter, melted
3 tablespoons Worcestershire
    sauce
1/2 teaspoon garlic powder
1/4 teaspoon onion salt
1/4 teaspoon seasoned salt

1 7-ounce package wheat nuts
2 cups Nabisco Twigs® Sesame
    and Cheese Snack Sticks
1 12-ounce can deluxe mixed
    nuts
1 3-ounce package pork rinds,
    broken into bite-
    sized pieces

Directions
1. Preheat oven to 250 degrees.
2. In large bowl, combine first 5 ingredients.
3. To same bowl, add remaining ingredients in order given. Stir well to coat until all liquid is absorbed.
4. Coat sheet cake pan with non-stick cooking spray.
5. Onto pan, spread mixture evenly.
6. Bake 45 minutes, stirring every 15 minutes.

1 Serving

Protein 11

13
Net Carbs

15 Carbs

2 Fiber

15

Easy **Low Carb Creations**
for kids

Don't be a Falling Star...

Falling Stars Burn Out

Peanut Butter and Jelly Sandwich

55 Net Carbs

Hostess® Twinkie™

25 Net Carbs

Krispie Kreme® Chocolate Iced Glazed Dougnut

33 Net Carbs

Easy **Low Carb Creations** for kids

Start Now, Eat Later

> 15

Net Carbs

2 Cheddar Apple Pizza 76

9 Chocolate Peanut Butter Mousse 77

0 Finger Gelatin 78

9 Fruit Fluff 79

14 Peanut Butter and "Jelly" Parfait . .80

2 Spiced Almonds 82

4 Strawberry White Chocolate Mouse 83

I'm *Starving*

< 15

Net Carbs

7 Peanut Butter Play Dough 81

Sweet Stars

Cheddar Apple Pizza

Makes 12 servings

4 tablespoons butter, melted
2 cups pecans, very finely
chopped
2 tablespoons Splenda®

2 large baking apples, peeled, cut
into 1/4-inch slices
1 cup shredded cheddar cheese

1/2 cup Brown Sugar Twin®
1/2 cup chopped pecans
1/2 teaspoon ground cinnamon
1/2 teaspoon ground nutmeg

3 tablespoons cold butter

Directions
1. Preheat oven to 400 degrees.
2. In medium bowl, add first 3 ingredients and stir well.
3. Coat 12-inch pizza pan with non-stick cooking spray.
4. Into pizza pan, press pecan mixture to form crust.
5. Bake crust 8 minutes. Remove from oven; reduce oven temperature to 350 degrees.
6. Onto crust, arrange all apple slices in single layer in a circular pattern.
7. On top of apples, sprinkle cheese evenly.
8. In small bowl, combine next 4 ingredients; sprinkle over cheese.
9. Cut butter into small pieces; dot top of pizza with butter.
10. Bake 20 minutes or until apples are tender.
11. Serve warm.

Chocolate Peanut Butter Mousse

Makes 6 servings / 1/2 cup each

2 ounces cream cheese, softened
3 tablespoons peanut butter
1 tablespoon Splenda®

1 cup whipping cream

1 cup water

1 package sugar-free chocolate
    instant pudding mix

Directions

1. In medium bowl, add first 3
    ingredients; beat 1 minute
    with electric mixer.
2. Add whipping cream and
    beat until thickened.
3. Add water and beat again.
4. Add pudding mix and mix 1
    minute.
5. Pour into 6 dessert dishes;
    cover and refrigerate 1 hour.

May substitute sugar-free
butterscotch instant pudding mix.

Easy Low Carb Creations
for kids

Finger Gelatin
Makes 24 servings

1 Serving

0

1 Protein

Net Carbs

0 Fiber

0 Carbs

15

Easy
Low Carb Creations
for kids

3 .3-ounce packages sugar-free gelatin (choose your favorite flavor)

4 .25-ounce packages unflavored gelatin

4 cups boiling water

1 cup cold water

Directions

1. In 9 x 13-inch glass baking dish, combine first 2 ingredients. Stir gelatins together until well blended.
2. To gelatin, slowly add boiling water, stirring until dissolved.
3. To same dish, add cold water; stir.
4. Chill 2 hours or until firm. Cut into squares or use cookie cutters to make fun shapes. For holidays and special occasions, use canned pasteurized sweetened whipped cream, raisins, and/or fruit pieces to decorate.

Fruit Fluff

Makes 16 servings / 1/2 cup each

2 .3-ounce packages sugar-free orange gelatin

1 24-ounce container small curd cottage cheese

2 11-ounce cans mandarin oranges, drained

1 8-ounce carton whipped topping

Directions
1. In large bowl, stir together dry gelatin, cottage cheese and mandarin oranges until well blended.
2. Fold in whipped topping.
3. Cover and chill 1 hour.

Variations:

Substitute lime gelatin and use crushed pineapple.

Substitute strawberry gelatin and use chopped strawberries

1 Serving

Protein 9

9
Net Carbs

10 Carbs

0 Fiber

15

Easy Low Carb Creations for kids

Peanut Butter and "Jelly" Parfait
Makes 12 servings

1 cup peanuts
12 5-ounce paper cups

1 8-ounce package cream cheese
1/2 cup peanut butter
1/4 cup Splenda®

1 8-ounce carton whipped
    topping, divided

1/4 cup grape Simply Fruit®
1 cup red seedless grapes, halved

Directions
1. Into paper cups, place an equal amount of peanuts. Set aside.
2. Into medium bowl, place next 3 ingredients; beat with electric mixer until creamy.
3. To same bowl, add 2 cups whipped topping; beat until well blended. Set aside.
4. Into remaining whipped topping, stir grape Simply Fruit® spread until well blended.
5. Over peanuts in cups, place equal amounts of grape natural fruit spread/whipped topping mixture. Spread over peanuts to edges of cups.
6. On top of grape natural fruit spread/whipped topping mixture, place equal amounts of peanut butter mixture. Spread evenly to edges of cups.
7. Top peanut butter mixture with 4 or 5 grape halves. Cover and chill.

Peanut Butter Play Dough
Makes 16 servings /2 tablespoons each*

1 cup peanut butter
2 tablespoons honey
1/4 cup Splenda®
1 cup nonfat dry milk

Directions
1. Into medium bowl, combine all ingredients. Stir well.
2. If too sticky, add more dry milk.
3. Have fun creating animals, flowers, and other things with your playdough.
4. When finished playing, place play dough in tightly covered container in the refrigerator. When ready to play again, bring to room temperature.

If too dry, add a little peanut butter and mix well.

*This is really just to be nibbled on while playing.

1 Serving
Protein 5
7
Net Carbs
8 Carbs
1 Fiber
< 15

Easy **Low Carb Creations** for kids

Spiced Almonds

Makes 16 servings/approximately 1/4 cup each

1 egg white
1 tablespoon water

1 teaspoon vanilla
1 teaspoon salt
1 tablespoon cinnamon
1/2 teaspoon nutmeg
1 cup Splenda®

1 pound whole almonds

Directions
1. Preheat oven to 300 degrees.
2. In large bowl, beat egg white and water with electric mixer until foamy.
3. To beaten egg whites, add next 5 ingredients; beat until well blended.
4. To same bowl, add almonds; stir until well coated.
5. Coat 9 x 13-inch pan with non-stick cooking spray.
6. Into pan, spread almond mixture evenly.
7. Bake 45 minutes, stirring every 15 minutes.

Easy
Low Carb Creations
for kids

Strawberry White Chocolate Mousse

Makes 6 servings/approximately 1/2 cup each

2 ounces cream cheese, softened
5 strawberries
1 tablespoon Splenda®

1 cup whipping cream

1 cup water

1 package sugar-free white
    chocolate instant pudding
    mix

Directions

1. In medium bowl, add first 3 ingredients; beat 1 minute with electric mixer.
2. Add whipping cream and beat until thickened.
3. Add water and beat again.
4. Add pudding mix and mix 1 minute.
5. Pour into 6 dessert dishes; cover and refrigerate at least 1 hour.

1 Serving
1 Protein
4 Net Carbs
5 Carbs
1 Fiber

15

Easy Low Carb Creations
for kids

Don't be a Falling Star...

Falling Stars Burn Out

Canned Corn 1/2 cup serving

14 Net Carbs

Regular-size French Fries from Long John Silvers®

31 Net Carbs

Regular-size Onion Rings from A & W

43 Net Carbs

Easy Low Carb Creations for kids

*Sta*rt Now, Eat Later

Net Carbs

Bacon Bean Bundles 87

Parmesan Zucchini Bites
. . . . 90

I'm *Star*ving

Net Carbs

14 Ants on a Log
. . . . 86

6 Celery Peanut Butter Sailboats
. . . . 88

8 Celery Strawberry Logs 89

Veggie Stars

Easy **Low Carb Creations**
for kids

Ants on a Log

Makes 1 serving

2 5- inch long celery sticks

2 tablespoons peanut butter

10 raisins

< 15

1 Serving

14 Net Carbs

8 Protein

3 Fiber

17 Carbs

Directions
1. Wash celery; dry it with paper towels.
2. Use butter knife to fill celery with peanut butter.
3. Place 5 ants (raisins) on each log (celery filled with peanut butter).

Easy **Low Carb Creations** for kids

Bacon Bean Bundles
Makes 8 servings

1 pound fresh green beans

8 slices bacon

1/2 teaspoon onion salt
8 toothpicks

Directions
1. Preheat oven to 400 degrees.
2. Remove ends from beans; wash beans thoroughly.
3. In medium saucepan, place beans; cover with water.
4. Over high heat, bring water to boil; cook 6 minutes or until tender. Drain.
5. Meanwhile, in skillet over medium-high heat, cook bacon 4 minutes to partially cook.
6. Remove bacon from skillet; place it on paper towel.
7. Divide beans into 8 equal bundles of 9 or 10 beans.
8. Wrap bacon strip around each bean bundle and secure with toothpick.
9. Coat sheet cake pan with non-stick cooking spray.
10. Place Bacon Bean Bundles on sheet cake pan.
11. Sprinkle beans evenly with onion salt.
12. Bake 15-20 minutes or until bacon is crisp.

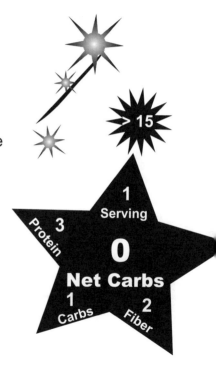

> 15

1 Serving
3 Protein
0 Net Carbs
1 Carbs
2 Fiber

Easy Low Carb Creations for kids

Celery Peanut Butter Sailboats

Makes 1 serving

2 5-inch long celery sticks

2 tablespoons peanut butter

.5 ounces salami slices
6 toothpicks

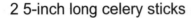

Directions
1. Wash celery; dry it with paper towels.
2. Use butter knife to fill celery with peanut butter.
3. Cut 6 2-inch triangles out of salami slices.
4. Place a toothpick in each triangle to make a sail.
5. Place 3 toothpick/salami sails into each boat.

1 Serving
10 Protein
6
Net Carbs
3 Fiber
9 Carbs

< 15

Celery Strawberry Logs

Makes 1 serving

2 5-inch long celery sticks

2 tablespoons strawberry cream
      cheese

Directions
1. Wash celery; dry it with paper towels.
2. Use butter knife to fill celery with strawberry cream cheese.

< 15

1 Serving
Protein 2
8 Net Carbs
9 Carbs
1 Fiber

Easy
Low Carb Creations
for kids

Parmesan Zucchini Bites

Makes 8 servings / 1/2 cup each

1
Serving

2
Protein

1
Net Carbs

0
Fiber

1
Carbs

Easy
Low Carb Creations
for kids

4 small zucchinis

2 eggs

1/2 cup Parmesan cheese
1/4 teaspoon salt
1/8 teaspoon pepper

Directions
1. Preheat oven to 450 degrees.
2. Wash zucchinis. Cut each one into 1/4-inch round slices.
3. In small bowl, place eggs; beat slightly.
4. In separate bowl, place remaining ingredients; stir.
5. Coat sheet cake pan with non-stick cooking spray.
6. Dip zucchini pieces in egg, then in Parmesan cheese mixture and place in single layer on sheet cake pan.
7. Bake 20-25 minutes or until crispy.

Index

A

Ants on a Log 86

B

B.B.Q. Wings. 49
Bacon Bean Bundles. 87
Bacon Tomato Stars 48
Banana Split Dessert. 34
Benefits of Eating Healthy
      Foods 8-9
Berry Smoothie 42
Broccoli, Cheese, Ham
      Roll-Ups. 50

C

Celery Peanut Butter
      Sailboats 88
Celery Strawberry Logs. 89
Cheddar Almonds 64
Cheddar Apple Pizza. 76
Cheddar Bacon Almonds. . . . 65
Cheddar Bacon Pork Rinds. . 66
Cheddar Pork Rinds 67

Cheese Dip with Vegetables . 28
Cherry Almond Cheesecake
      Cookies 20
Chicken Drumettes 51
Chipped Beef Dip 29
Chocolate Brownie Meringues 21
Chocolate Peanut Butter
      Mousse 77
Chocolate White Chocolate
      Pops 35
Coconut Macaroons 22

Cookies

Cherry Almond Cheesecake
      Cookies 20
Chocolate Brownie
      Meringues 21
Coconut Macaroons 22
Lemon Meringue Cookies. . 23
Peanut Butter Cookies 24
Strawberry Pecan Cheesecake
      Cookies 25
Cooking Terms. 17
Cranberry, Strawberry Yogurt
      Pops 36
Creamy Orange Yogurt
      Pops 37

D

Dairy Carb Counts. 11
Dill Dip with Vegetables. 30
Dill Pickle Canoes 68
Dill Pickle Sailboats 69

Dips

Cheese Dip with Vegetables 28
Chipped Beef Dip 29
Dill Dip with Vegetables . . . 30
Fruity Fruit Dip 31

Drinks

Berry Smoothie. 42
Lemon Shake-ups 43
Orange Julius 44
Peach Coolers 45

F

Finger Gelatin 78
Food Preparation
      Terms. 16-17
Frozen Pops 38

Frozen Treats

Banana Split Dessert. 34
Chocolate White Chocolate
      Pops 35

Easy **Low Carb Creations**
for kids

Cranberry, Strawberry Yogurt
    Pops 36
Creamy Orange Yogurt
    Pops 37
    Frozen Pops 38
    Vanilla Ice Cream 39
Fruit Carb Count 12
Fruity Fruit Dip 31
Fruit Fluff 79

H

Ham and Cheese Cups 52
Ham and Cheese Pizza
    Wraps 53
Ham Kabobs 54
How to Eat Low Carb 10

L

Layered Tex-Mex Bowls 55
Lemon Meringue Cookies . . . 23
Lemon Shake-ups 43

M

Meal Makers
    Bacon Tomato Stars 48
    B.B.Q. Wings 49
    Broccoli, Cheese, Ham
        Roll-Ups 50
    Chicken Drumettes 51
    Ham and Cheese Cups . . . 52
    Ham and Cheese Pizza
        Wraps 53
    Ham Kabobs 54
    Layered Tex-Mex Bowls . . . 55
    Pepperoni Pizza Wraps . . . 56
    Sausage Kabobs 57
    Sweet and Sour Dogs 58
    Tex-Mex Dogs 59
    Tuna Salad Canoes 60
    Turkey Kabobs 61
Measuring Information 17

N

Nuts and Seeds Carb
    Counts 11

O

Orange Julius 44

P

Parmesan Zucchini Bites 90
Peach Coolers 45
Peanut Butter and
    "Jelly" Parfait 80
Peanut Butter Cookies 24
Peanut Butter Playdough . . . 81
Pepperoni Pizza Wraps 56

R

Ranch Almonds 70
Ranch Pork Rinds 71

S

Salty Crunchy Snacks
    Cheddar Almonds 64
    Cheddar Bacon Almonds . . 65
    Cheddar Bacon Pork
        Rinds 66
    Cheddar Pork Rinds 67
    Dill Pickle Canoes 68

Dill Pickle Sailboats 69
Ranch Almonds 70
Ranch Pork Rinds 71
Savory Almonds 72
Savory Mix 73
Sanitation 16
Sausage Kabobs 57
Savory Almonds 72
Savory Mix 73
Spiced Almonds 82
Star Symbols Explained 6-7
Strawberry Pecan Cheesecake
    Cookies 25
Strawberry White Chocolate
    Mousse 83

Sweets
Cheddar Apple Pizza 76
Chocolate Peanut Butter
    Mousse 77
Finger Gelatin 78
Fruit Fluff 79
Peanut Butter and
    "Jelly" Parfait 80
Peanut Butter Play Dough . 81
Spiced Almonds 82
Strawberry White Chocolate
    Mousse 83

Sweet and Sour Dogs 58

T

Tex-Mex Dogs 59
Tips for Low Carb
    Eating 13-15
Tuna Salad Canoes 60
Turkey Kabobs 61

V

Vanilla Ice Cream 39
Vegetable Carb Counts 12
Vegetables
Ants on a Log 86
Bacon Bean Bundles 87
Celery Peanut Butter
    Sailboats 88
Celery Strawberry Logs . . . 89
Parmesan Zucchini Bites . . 90

About the Authors

Jackie Bible is a professional home economist with 19 years experience in teaching high school students nutrition and food preparation. She enjoys developing, altering and preparing her creations for family and friends.

Lori Overmyer teaches high school journalism and English. She also instructs design and photography at Indiana University's High School Journalism Institute. Lori's computer design skills and love of cooking combine to create pleasing recipe layouts that are easy to follow.

Curious? The Experts Say...

I have been an advocate of high protein/low carb diets for the past 4 - 5 years and believe it is safe and effective. In fact it should be viewed as a different way of eating rather than a "diet". It is particularly effective for those who are overweight, diabetic or who have high triglyceride levels or low HDL levels. I would avoid it in people with advance kidney disease because of the high protein load and I would still attempt to minimize the use of saturated fats - especially in those with documented coronary disease.

Basil Genetos, MD and FACC

I have always shunned the latest fad diets and urged my patients to eat a balanced diet. I realize now that the diet advice I have been giving for the past 20 years is flawed, since for most Americans a "balanced" diet has too heavily emphasized carbohydrates. I realize now that you can reduce your carbohydrate intake, lose weight, and eat a truly balanced diet.

Rose Wenrich, MD

For additional copies of **Easy Low Carb Creations for Kids** or a copy of **Easy Low Carb Creations**, contact the authors through the **Easy Low Carb Creations** web site at www.easylowcarbcreations.com

Easy **Low Carb Creations for kids**